11+ CLOZE TESTS

Book 1

Word Bank Tests A-F

Multiple Choice Tests A-F

Partial Words Tests A-F

How to use this pack to make the most of 11+ exam preparation

It is important to remember that for 11+ exams there is no national syllabus, no pass mark and no retake option! It is therefore vitally important that your child is fully primed in order to perform to the best of their ability to give themselves the best possible chance on the day.

Unlike similar publications, the First Past the Post® series uniquely assesses your child's performance on a question-by-question basis relative to peers helping to identify areas for improvement and further practice.

Cloze Tests

Cloze Tests consist of passages with missing words that require the child to recognise and select the correct answer from a set of several options presented. Both comprehension and vocabulary are tested.

Never has it been more useful to learn from mistakes!

Students can improve by as much as 15 percent, not only by focused practice but also by targeting any weak areas.

How to manage your child's own practice

To get the most up-to-date information, log on to the ElevenPlusExams website (www.elevenplusexams.co.uk). ElevenPlusExams is the largest UK on-line resource with over 40,000 webpages and a forum administered by a select group of experienced moderators.

About the authors

The ElevenPlusExams **First Past the Post®** series has been created by a team of experienced tutors and authors from leading British universities including Oxford and Cambridge.

Published by University of Buckingham Press

With special thanks to the children who tested our material at the ElevenPlusExams centre in Harrow.

ISBN: 9781908684288

elevenplusexams
head for success

About Us

ElevenPlusExams is the UK's largest website offering advice, information, a moderated forum, books, downloadable e-papers, interactive downloadable software and interactive on-line games to enhance your child's chances of success in the demanding selective schools entrance exams, namely 11+ and common entrance exams.

The company also provides 11+ tuition and is a supplier of software and paper products to schools, tutors, and the public.

ElevenPlusExams is a trusted and authoritative source of information and advice. It has been quoted in numerous national newspapers (including The Telegraph, The Sunday Observer, The Daily Mail, The Sunday Telegraph), BBC Radio and national television (BBC1 and Channel 4).

Set up in July 2004, the website grew from an initial 20 webpages to more than 40,000 today. By ElevenPlusExam's conservative counter, nearly 4 million parents have visited the website, however Google, who places strategic adverts on the website, has statistics that put the visitors at several this figure.

The website gives parents impartial advice on preparation, techniques, 11+ exams in their area and preparation material based on actual experience. The forum is the largest for 11+ in the UK, and is moderated by over 20 experts including parents, experienced tutors and authors who collectively provide support both before the exams, and for those parents who are also unfortunate enough to have to appeal the decisions.

The website also serves as a notice board for mock exams, intensive courses and long term courses in the country as well as hosting an extensive 11+ book shop.

Visit our website to benefit from the wealth of information and advice and see why we are the market's leading 'one-stop-shop' for all your eleven plus needs.

- ✓ Comprehensive quality content and advice written by 11+ experts

- ✓ 11+ Shop supplying a wide range of books, e-papers, software and apps

- ✓ UK's largest online 11+ Forum moderated by experts

- ✓ Lots of FREE practice papers to download

- ✓ Professional tuition services optimising state of the art technology

- ✓ Short Intensive 11+ courses

- ✓ Year long 11+ courses

- ✓ Mock exams tailored to mirror those of the main examining bodies

There are three Cloze passage question types included in this book that are designed to prepare your child for the new styles of 11 plus exams. We recommend these tests be used as real exam practice to benchmark your child's performance and gauge your child's reading, comprehension and vocabulary levels.

Word Bank Cloze Tests

These comprise passages in which several words are omitted and placed in a 'word bank' or list. The objective is to insert the correct words from the list into the appropriate blank spaces. This type of question relies on the child's understanding of the passage content to ascertain the accurate answer.

Multiple Choice Cloze Tests

Multiple Choice Cloze Tests consist of passages with missing words that require the child to recognise a correct answer from a set of three possible options. As well as testing vocabulary, these exercises also test how efficiently words are used in their correct context.

Partial Words Cloze Tests

Partial Words Cloze Tests include words in which several characters are missing, requiring the child to add the deliberately omitted letters from each word. The content of the passages provide clues to the incomplete words and tests the child's vocabulary.

Contents Page

Contents Page

Once you have completed each test and marked them using the answers at the back you can anonymously go online and compare your child's performance relative to peers who have completed the same test(s) using our 11+ Peer Compare System™.

You can register by visiting www.ElevenPlusExams.co.uk/FirstPastThePost using the access code supplied with this publication.

BLANK PAGE

FIRST PAST THE POST® SERIES

Cloze Tests
Word Bank

Marking Grid						
Test	A	B	C	D	E	F
Score						
	/24	/16	/26	/20	/17	/29

Read the following instructions carefully:

1. Choose the correct words from the word bank to complete the following passages.

2. The timer indicates the maximum recommended time you have for the following passages.

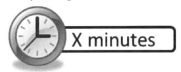 X minutes

3. Work as quickly and carefully as you can.

4. When you have finished a page, go straight onto the next page until you finish the test.

5. Write your answers clearly and legibly. You will get no marks for illegible answers.

6. To change your answer, rub out your old answer completely and then mark your new answer clearly.

7. When you reach the end of a test, go back and check all your answers in the remaining time.

8. If you cannot answer a question, go on to the next question.

Good luck!

After you have finished this paper you can use the <u>11+ Peer Compare System</u>™ to see how well you performed compared to others who have taken these tests. You can register by visiting <u>www.ElevenPlusExams.co.uk/FirstPastThePost</u> to post your results anonymously and obtain the feedback.

Word Bank

adventure	home	cacophony	altercation	emerged	talkative
escalated	longing	abhorrent	recent	trepidation	solitude

The Altercation

The subdued man **(1)**_____ from the station relatively unscathed and immensely relieved

to be away from the **(2)**_____ crowd. He was somewhat bewildered at how a minor

(3)_____ on the train had swiftly **(4)**_____ into a barrage of obnoxious

insults towards him.

He was neither **(5)**_____ nor confident by nature, preferring the **(6)**_____ of

his own company and the petrifying incident left him **(7)**_____ for the familiarity and

tranquillity of his **(8)**_____. The constant **(9)**_____ of the city no longer

enthralled him and the **(10)**_____ confrontation only served to increase his feelings of

melancholy and **(11)**_____. That was when he knew his short-lived

(12)_____ was over.

Word Bank

seldom	efficient	enables	murky	acute	maintain
equipped	malicious	enormous	refined	cartilage	bulky

Sharks

Sharks are a type of fish but unlike other fish, they have **(13)**_____ instead of bones, which

is lighter and **(14)**_____ sharks to swim faster. One of the most **(15)**_____

sharks is the great white shark although it **(16)**_____ attacks people. Despite being

(17)_____ creatures sometimes weighing more than 4,000 pounds, sharks do not sink as

their livers are well **(18)**_____ to hold a lot of oil, which helps them to float and

(19)_____ their balance in the water.

Sharks are highly **(20)**_____ predators and have an **(21)**_____ sense of

smell, hearing and sight.

So **(22)**_____ are their senses, that in the water, they are able to smell their prey from

(23)_____ distances and their eyes can see clearly even in the **(24)**_____

light of the ocean's depths.

Word Bank

collided	minute	waves	atmosphere	debris	Gravity
Earth					

The Moon

Scientists believe that the Moon was formed 4.6 billion years ago from the **(1)**_____ that

was left over when a rock the size of Mars **(2)**_____ into the Earth.

The Moon has virtually no **(3)**_____, therefore no sound can be heard on it. This is because

light and sound waves bounce off **(4)**_____ particles in the atmosphere and without it,

sound **(5)**_____ cannot travel.

(6)_____ on the Moon is approximately one-sixth of what it is on Earth, therefore the

space suits worn by astronauts weigh 180 pounds on **(7)**_____ but only 30 pounds on the

Moon.

Word Bank

acquired	arachnophobia	irrational	phobia	heightened	specific
anxiety	agitated	bizarre			

Phobias

A phobia is an **(8)**_____ fear that a person feels only when faced with a particular object or

in a **(9)**_____ situation. Approximately one in ten people suffer from a

(10)_____, many of which are likely to have been **(11)**_____ during

childhood.

Common phobias include: a **(12)**_____ fear of spiders which is also known as

(13)_____, a fear of heights (acrophobia), and dogs (cynophobia). Phobias that are more

(14)_____ include: a fear of mirrors, a fear of washing or cleaning (ablutophobia), and a

fear of sleep (hypnophobia).

People who have severe phobias often feel immense **(15)**_____ and consciously avoid

situations they know will make them feel **(16)**_____, panicky and in some cases, nauseous.

Word Bank

responsible	species	river	shallow	longest	equivalent
impressive	tributaries	oceans	length	savage	second
snake	gallons				

The Amazon River

Located in South America, the colossal Amazon River is 4,000 miles long and is the second

(1)_____ river in the world, after the River Nile. It is also considered the broadest

(2)_____, carrying more water than the Mississippi, Nile and Yangtze rivers combined. It is

(3)_____ for about one-fifth of the fresh water that flows into the world's

(4)_____. There are no bridges across the entire (5)_____ of the river. The

(6)_____ Amazon has more than 1,000 (7)_____ - streams or smaller rivers

that flow into a main river. The river is inhabited by thousands of (8)_____ of plants,

animals and fish, including the (9)_____ carnivorous piranha and the anaconda

(10)_____, which is found in the (11)_____ waters of the river. The Amazon

pours 60 million (12)_____ of water into the Atlantic Ocean every (13)_____

and the amount of water that flows through it each day is (14)_____ to the total amount

of water used in New York City over 12 years.

Word Bank

commence	heralded	country	British	emperor	independence
commemorate	visited	waterfront	ceremonial	monument	construction

Gateway of India

The Gateway of India is a huge stone arch **(15)**_____ built by the Indian government to

(16)_____ the landing of King George V, **(17)**_____ of India during British

rule, and his wife Queen Mary, when they **(18)**_____ India in 1911.

However, they only managed to see a cardboard model of the edifice since **(19)**_____ of

the monument did not **(20)**_____ until 1915, and was completed nine years later in 1924.

Designed by Scotsman George Wittet and located on the Mumbai **(21)**_____ overlooking

the Arabian Sea, the Gateway of India became the **(22)**_____ entrance to India for

Viceroys and the new Governors of Mumbai. It was a **(23)**_____ symbol of the power of

the British Empire.

Following India's **(24)**_____ which signalled the end of British rule, the last

(25)_____ troops left the **(26)**_____ passing through the gateway in a

ceremony in 1948.

Word Bank

perception	conscripted	architecture	edifice	network	Dynasty
continuous	cemetery	plateaus	laborious	resplendent	importance
scenery	world	disgraced	enhanced	sections	construction
emperors	heritage				

The Great Wall of China

China is a land of beautiful **(1)**_____, ancient temples with thousands of years of rich

cultural **(2)**_____, and is home to the longest man-made structure in the

(3)_____, the Great Wall of China.

Built over a period of 2,000 years, the **(4)**_____ structure spans approximately 4,000 miles

across China's deserts, mountains and **(5)**_____.

Contrary to many people's **(6)**_____ of the Great Wall being one **(7)**_____

mammoth structure, it is in fact a **(8)**_____ of many individual wall segments that were

built at various times and by multiple **(9)**_____ to protect the Chinese empire from its

enemies.

Although work began as early as 221 BC by the first emperor of China, many **(10)**_____ of

the wall have since been rebuilt and **(11)**_____. The majority of the existing wall was reconstructed during the Ming (12)_____ from 1368 to 1644.

Building the wall was a challenging and (13)_____ task, often undertaken in unbearable

working conditions by more than 300,000 prisoners, peasants and (14)_____ noblemen.

Not only did they have to endure backbreaking work, they were (15)_____ to leave their

families for several years at a time to construct the (16)_____.

Working on the wall was so hazardous that during its (17)_____, the Great Wall was

referred to as 'the longest (18)_____ on Earth', because more than one million people lost

their lives building it. So appealing is its (19)_____ and historical

(20)_____, that the Great Wall attracts as many as ten million visitors each year.

Word Bank

region	integral	winter	nourishment	solely	ice
frozen	sledges	paramount	survive	environment	hostile
relationship	meat	diet	prey	inhabited	

The Inuit

The Arctic area of North America is one of the most remote and **(1)**_____ places on Earth.

Despite this, it is **(2)**_____ by four million Inuit people. During the bleak

(3)_____ months, the entire **(4)**_____ is frozen and the Inuit are forced to

(5)_____ in sub-zero temperatures with no daylight. Their survival in such conditions is

(6)_____ dependent upon their vast knowledge and understanding of their

(7)_____. Hunting and fishing is of **(8)**_____ importance to the Inuit people

and is their only means of **(9)**_____. Their **(10)**_____ consists of whale,

walrus, moose and seal **(11)**_____, which they find by waiting at air holes the seals make in

the **(12)**_____. Their **(13)**_____ with animals is not limited to being that of

hunter and **(14)**_____; dogs are an **(15)**_____ part of their lives and are

relied upon to pull **(16)**_____ across many miles of **(17)**_____ sea.

Word Bank

unsanitary	recuperation	campaign	inventing	destitute	elected
vocation	humanitarian	fortunate	procedures	destiny	mortality
wounded	nature	hospitals	heroine	earning	profound
arrangement	regard	influential	nursing	significant	located
training	desires	era	statistician	profession	

Florence Nightingale

Florence Nightingale was born in 1820 and was a celebrated social reformer and **(1)**_____.

Although raised in a period where women's sole occupation was to marry well and bear children,

Florence always believed that her **(2)**_____ lay in something greater. Her profound

religious faith instilled a strong moral duty to help the less **(3)**_____.

Against the **(4)**_____ of her parents, her belief in God led to a growing conviction that

nursing was to be her **(5)**_____. Florence's parents eventually relented and gave their

permission for her to undertake three months **(6)**_____ training at a hospital in Germany.

She is most acclaimed for serving as a nurse and tending to **(7)**_____ soldiers during the

Crimean War. Cholera and malaria were rife among the British soldiers **(8)**_____ in army

hospitals in Turkey, where Florence volunteered her services. Upon her arrival, she was appalled by the

(9)_____ and harsh conditions that unsurprisingly contributed to the high

(10)_____ rate amongst the wounded and disease-ridden soldiers.

Florence thus embarked on a mission to organise the (11)_____ and improve supplies of

blankets, beds and food, as well as raise the standard of cleanliness. Her benevolent

(12)_____ knew no bounds and she often checked on the soldiers during the night with

the aid of a lamp, (13)_____her the name 'Lady with the Lamp'.

Upon her return to Britain, Florence was deemed a (14)_____ for her extraordinary efforts

and revolutionary thinking. Furthermore, her insightful reforms and ideas have had a

(15)_____ influence on the nature of modern healthcare, and her tireless

(16)_____ to improve health standards and hospital planning continue to be held in high

(17)_____.

Prior to Florence's (18)_____ efforts in the field of nursing, the profession held negative

connotations and was considered appropriate only for (19)_____ women. However,

through her noble efforts she successfully transformed nursing into an honourable

(20)_____ for women, and in 1860 was instrumental in establishing the first professional

(21)_____ school for nurses.

Florence's influence on nursing is evident today, particularly in the (22)_____ of hospital

wards, which are based on her assessment that the way in which a hospital is designed, has a

(23)_____ impact on the health and recovery of patients. Moreover, the introduction of

her pioneering infection control (24)_____ combined with a healthy diet, continues to be

recognised as key factors assisting the (25)_____ process.

Among Florence's numerous achievements, she is also credited with (26)_____ the pie

chart and subsequently became the first female to be (27)_____ to the Royal Statistical

Society, a position typically reserved for men during this (28)_____.

Florence died in 1910 at the age of 90, but not before becoming one of the most (29)_____

and famous women of the 19th century.

BLANK PAGE

FIRST PAST THE POST® SERIES

Cloze Tests
Multiple Choice

Marking Grid						
Test	A	B	C	D	E	F
Score	/17	/18	/19	/16	/19	/40

Read the following instructions carefully:

1. In the following questions carefully choose the correct word that fits the passage.

2. The timer indicates the maximum recommended time you have for the following passages.

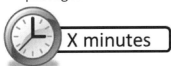

3. Work as quickly and carefully as you can.

4. When you have finished a page, go straight onto the next page until you finish the test.

5. To change your answer, rub out your old answer completely and then mark your new answer clearly.

6. If you are unsure of the answer then choose the one you think is most appropriate or return to it later.

7. When you reach the end of a test, go back and check all your answers in the remaining time.

8. If you cannot answer a question, go on to the next question.

Good luck!

After you have finished this paper you can use the 11+ Peer Compare System™ to see how well you performed compared to others who have taken these tests. You can register by visiting www.ElevenPlusExams.co.uk/FirstPastThePost to post your results anonymously and obtain the feedback.

Benjamin Franklin

1
☐ Founding
Born in 1706, Benjamin Franklin was one of the ☐ Foundling Fathers of the United States of America
☐ Foundered

2
☐ pivotal
and played a ☐ gratuitous role in America's struggle for independence.
☐ pivoted

3
☐ amateurish
An extremely ☐ unaccomplished man, Franklin was also a
☐ versatile

4
☐ cerebral
☐ celebrated politician, writer,
☐ undiscovered

5
☐ frequented
scientist and inventor, who ☐ frequently used his home as a laboratory for conducting electrical
☐ frequency

6
☐ discoveries
experiments. To this day, he is greatly admired for his ☐ desires and theories regarding
☐ desperation

7
☐ gas
☐ electricity .
☐ biology

8
☐ prominent
One of his most ☐ primed inventions was the lightning rod,
☐ medieval

9
☐ designated
☐ designed to protect buildings
☐ desiccated

10
☐ fire
from catching ☐ currents during electrical storms. This invention earned Franklin
☐ currants

11
☐ region
☐ worldwide
☐ marginal

12

fame and respect, and is still used to protect [   ]
- [   ] people
- [   ] towns   across the globe today.
- [   ] buildings

Volcanoes

13

Volcanoes are [   ]
- [   ] cavalries
- [   ] cavities   in the surface of the earth. Occasionally, a build-up of
- [   ] caves

14

- [   ] fissure
- [   ] pressured
- [   ] pressure

15

occurs that causes volcanoes to [   ]
- [   ] bashfully
- [   ] forcefully erupt and blast out hot ash, gas and lava. Sometimes, so
- [   ] gracefully

16

- [   ] vigorous
- [   ] vigilant   is the blast that it can send ash soaring as high as 17 miles into the air. The hot red
- [   ] vicarious

17

lava flows down the side of the volcano and [   ]
- [   ] solidifies
- [   ] fragments as it cools down.
- [   ] ferments

Earthquakes

1
☐ superficial
The ☐ peripheral surface of the Earth is made from ☐ infinitesimal pieces of rock called tectonic
☐ saturated

2
☐ colossal
☐ malleable

3
☐ accurately
plates. These are ☐ perpetually shifting and the point at which two plates ☐ conjoin   is known as
☐ pompously

4
☐ disconnect
☐ concur

5
☐ vigorous
a fault. This results in a build-up of ☐ insubstantial pressure between the plates, forcing the rocks to
☐ wavering

6
☐ absorb
☐ emit   waves of energy which travel to the Earth's surface. This sudden release of energy causes
☐ ooze

7
☐ transpire
the quake or tremor. It is estimated that thousands of earthquakes ☐ erupt   around the globe each
☐ disappear

8
☐ inaccessible
year, but many go undetected as they are either too weak or occur in remote, ☐ inconvenient areas.
☐ inconceivable

The Black Death

9 ☐ pandemic

The Black Death was a lethal ☐ distraction that ravaged Europe between 1347 and 1351. So

☐ illnesses

10

☐ insignificant

☐ trivial   was the outbreak, it claimed the lives of more than 75 million people globally, more

☐ virulent

11 ☐ moment   **12** ☐ squalid

than any other known ☐ illness   up until that time. The onset of the ☐ hygienic disease

☐ catastrophic   ☐ sanitary

created panic and hysteria throughout Britain. Like many medieval large cities, London had all the

13   **14** ☐ primitive

☐ innocuous

☐ associated problems of overcrowding and ☐ technological sanitation which ensured that

☐ haphazard   ☐ modern

15 ☐ population   **16** ☐ plague

contamination throughout the ☐ local   was inevitable. Many people believed the ☐ ravage

☐ resident   ☐ destroy

17 ☐ inflame

was a form of punishment for their sins and to ☐ alleviate   the wrath of God, they engaged in public

☐ exacerbate

18 ☐ penitence

acts of ☐ petulance   .

☐ retribution

Alexander Graham Bell

1
☐ obscure
Alexander Graham Bell was an ☐ ambiguous scientist and teacher of the deaf but is most
☐ illustrious

2
☐ celebrated
☐ calibrated   for inventing the telephone in 1876. He was born in Scotland in 1847 and for many years
☐ infamous

3
☐ transient
of his life had developed a ☐ ephemeral fascination with the idea of transmitting speech.
☐ profound

4
☐ device
It was while he was working at a school for deaf children that Bell fashioned a ☐ artefact that could
☐ code

5
☐ beam
transmit the human voice using an electric ☐ currant ; this came to be known as the telephone.
☐ current

6
☐ astronomical
His invention was an ☐ astrological   success and financially very

7
☐ profitable
☐ absorptive , which meant he
☐ meteoric
☐ prescriptive

8
☐ horseshoes
was able to contemplate other scientific inventions, including ☐ hydrofoils   and the metal detector.
☐ hieroglyphics

9
☐ fallacy
Bell died in 1922 but not without leaving a lasting ☐ legacy   for the world.
☐ autocracy

Thomas Edison

10 ☐ irresponsibly
Thomas Edison was born in 1847 and is ☐ irregularly   one of the greatest inventors and
☐ undeniably

11
☐ peers
☐ scrutineers of the 19th century.
☐ pioneers

12 ☐ scarcity   **13** ☐ affluence
He is credited with a ☐ multitude of inventions that have had a significant ☐ impact   on
☐ paucity   ☐ interference

14 ☐ motion
people's lives around the world. These include, among others; the electric motor, the ☐ motionless
☐ motivation

15 ☐ affable
picture, the phonograph and the ☐ affordable electric light.
☐ affluent

16 ☐ apathy
Edison's ☐ inquisitiveness in science was sparked at an early age and he was encouraged by his
☐ empathy

17 ☐ ardent
parents to pursue his ☐ denial passion.
☐ idle

18 ☐ patterned
By the time he died in 1931, he had ☐ patented   1,092 devices, thus making Edison the most
☐ painted

19
☐ prolific
☐ prophetic   inventor in history.
☐ unbecoming

Ancient Rome

1
☐ declining
Ancient Rome was a ☐ contemporary civilisation that began growing on the Italian Peninsula at the
☐ flourishing

2
☐ centenary
beginning of the eighth ☐ centuries BC. Gradually, the Roman Empire expanded to
☐ century

3
☐ eliminate
☐ encompass
☐ encroach

most of Western Europe, much of Asia, Northern Africa and the Mediterranean islands. At the height of

4
☐ sovereignty
its ☐ sovereign   around 150 AD , Rome controlled the greatest
☐ transience

5
☐ empire
☐ country ever seen in Europe up
☐ nation

to that time.

6
☐ liberated
Many of the ☐ conquered   nations benefited under Roman rule as the
☐ beleaguered

7
☐ disadvantaged
☐ undeveloped   road
☐ advanced

8
☐ unrestricted
system created by them enabled ☐ restricted   trade throughout the Empire increasing access to
☐ partial

9
☐ capacious
☐ copious   amounts of affordable goods. Subsequently, most conquered societies enjoyed greater
☐ Capricorn

10
- [ ] intensity
- [ ] prosperity under Roman rule, which overall presented them with a better way of
- [ ] destitution

11
- [ ] eating
- [ ] life .
- [ ] dressing

12
- [ ] minimal
- [ ] paramount importance to the Romans who held the belief that the Gods ultimately
- [ ] paltry

Religion was of

13
- [ ] controlled
- [ ] disciplined their lives and explanations of most events
- [ ] christened

14
- [ ] typically
- [ ] infrequently involved in divine
- [ ] typologically

15
- [ ] people
- [ ] nature both at home and in the
- [ ] deities

intervention. They spent vast amounts of time worshipping

16
- [ ] temples
- [ ] cenotaphs that were built throughout their Empire.
- [ ] monumental

numerous

The Human Brain

1

In relation to body size, humans have the largest brain which weighs ☐ appreciative
☐ approximately three pounds,
☐ admiringly

2

and is one of the most ☐ intricate parts of the human body that scientists still
☐ intrepid
☐ interim

3

☐ devour
☐ endeavour to
☐ ignored

understand.

4

It is made up of about 75 percent water and is one of the fattest ☐ organisms
☐ organs   in our body.
☐ limbs

5

The brain comprises several ☐ companies
☐ components and is the core of the human
☐ companions

6

☐ circulatory
☐ digestive   system,
☐ nervous

controlling everything from our thoughts and memories to decisions and movements.

7

The cerebrum is the largest of the four ☐ principle
☐ population brain components that constitutes up to 85
☐ principal

8

percent of the brain's ☐ impasse
☐ muse   and is associated with higher brain
☐ mass

9

☐ production
☐ function   .
☐ functional

10
- [ ] image
It is in this part of the brain where perception, [ ] imaginably , thought, judgement and decisions
- [ ] imagination

occur.

11
- [ ] complex
Our brains are [ ] informative and can do incredible things to help us
- [ ] controversial

12
- [ ] navigate
[ ] circumnavigate through
- [ ] conjugate

our busy lives and make sense of the world.

13
- [ ] cyclone
For instance, when you sleep your brain creates a [ ] velodrome that paralyses you to
- [ ] hormone

14
- [ ] premise
[ ] prevent
- [ ] persuade

you from acting out your dreams.

15
- [ ] generates
In addition, while you are awake, your brain [ ] thwarts between 11 and 23 watts of power; that is
- [ ] obstructs

16
- [ ] illuminate
enough energy to [ ] disable a light bulb!
- [ ] produce

17
- [ ] recalling
Although the brain stops growing when you reach 18, [ ] recanting memories or information helps you
- [ ] recasting

18
☐ connections

create new ☐ concoctions in your brain whatever age you are.
☐ enzymes

19
☐ entices

Creating new connections in the brain ☐ encircles your ability to process and remember information.
☐ enhances

St Paul's Cathedral

1
- [ ] apprehensive
- [ ] recognisable
- [ ] approachable

With its majestic dome, St Paul's Cathedral is one of London's most recognisable sights and has

2
- [ ] dominated
- [ ] sullied
- [ ] tainted

the city skyline for more than 300 years. However, throughout history, the

3
- [ ] conventional
- [ ] prosaic
- [ ] resplendent

4
- [ ] beguiled
- [ ] plagued
- [ ] charmed

cathedral has been plagued by grave misfortune and has had to be

5
- [ ] instructed
- [ ] broken
- [ ] reconstructed

on numerous occasions.

6
- [ ] dissolved
- [ ] engraved
- [ ] engulfed

The initial building was created in the year 604 but was tragically engulfed in a fire during a Viking

7
- [ ] inquest
- [ ] invasion
- [ ] invitation

8
- [ ] cathedral
- [ ] pens
- [ ] sanctuary

invasion in 962. Construction of a Gothic style cathedral commenced in 1087 following the

9
- [ ] advantageous
- [ ] calamitous
- [ ] constructive

Norman Conquest. Once again, another calamitous fire in 1136 caused significant delays, and it

10
- [ ] edifice
- [ ] orifice
- [ ] edible

was not for another 200 years that the edifice was finally completed in 1310.

11
☐ disappointing
Known as Old St Paul's, the cathedral was an enormous ☐ accomplishment at that time and was
☐ accompaniment

12
☐ purported
☐ threatened to be the largest medieval building throughout Europe. It was
☐ forbidden

13
☐ eligible
☐ excluded to have
☐ alleged

14
☐ sapphire
the world's tallest ☐ spire   and some of the finest stained glass windows.
☐ sphere

15
☐ Monarchs
☐ Nomads   and
☐ Mobsters

16
☐ censorship
noblemen often attended Mass, the official ☐ apprenticeship service of Catholicism and court business
☐ worship

17
☐ conducted
was sometimes ☐ convoluted in the church. Old St Paul stood tall and
☐ cancelled

18
☐ yielding
☐ unyielding until several
☐ pliable

19
☐ impeccability
centuries later, suffering from wear and tear, it began crumbling into a state of ☐ depression   .
☐ dilapidation

20
☐ exaggerated
Further tragedy ☐ besieged   the cathedral in 1561, when the spire burned down after being struck
☐ benefitted

21
☐ hail
by   ☐ lightning . It was during this time that the
☐ lighting

22
☐ lackadaisical
☐ indifferent   architect, Sir Christopher Wren,
☐ distinguished

23
☐ domain
recommended the tower be taken down and replaced with a classical ☐ dome   ; a design inspired by
☐ sphere

24

[ ] architecture

Parisian church [ ] archaeologists which was greatly admired by Wren.

[ ] librarians

25

However, before the project had even begun it had to be abandoned as another [ ] apostrophe

[ ] catastrophe

[ ] cacophony

26

[ ] covered

occurred in 1667 when the Great Fire of London [ ] ravaged through the narrow streets, reducing St

[ ] swayed

27   **28**

[ ] charred   [ ] immersion

Paul's to [ ] branded timbers and ash. In the [ ] aftermath of the raging inferno, Wren was

[ ] churlish   [ ] cohesion

29

[ ] commissioned

[ ] commiserated   to build a new cathedral in 1675.

[ ] commemorated

30

[ ] medieval

In comparison to previous [ ] Tudor   cathedrals that took centuries to construct, Wren's

[ ] Roman

31   **32**

[ ] mastication   [ ] mediocre

[ ] personification was completed in only 35 years and was the most [ ] trifling   building project

[ ] masterpiece   [ ] prodigious

33

[ ] prominent

of that time. Featuring baroque designs and a [ ] darken   dome, the awe-inspiring cathedral that

[ ] problematic

34 ☐ charisma
☐ ingenious
☐ gracious

stands today is a result of Wren's ☐ ingenious artistic vision and one that

35 ☐ occupies
☐ preoccupies a
☐ defies

significant place in London's history.

36 ☐ prescription
☐ inscription
☐ conscription

Upon his death in 1723, Wren was buried in St Pauls Cathedral and a Latin ☐ inscription   near his

37 ☐ infers
☐ translates
☐ transcends

tomb ☐ translates   to, 'Reader, if you seek his monument, look around you.'

38 ☐ notable
☐ frivolous
☐ inconsequential

Other ☐ frivolous   figures buried in the

39 ☐ alcoves
☐ belfry
☐ crypts

☐ belfry   of St Paul's Cathedral include the

40 ☐ ghastly
☐ military   heroes Lord Nelson and the Duke of Wellington.
☐ loathed

FIRST PAST THE POST® SERIES

Cloze Tests
Partial Words

Marking Grid						
Test	A	B	C	D	E	F
Score						
	/17	/23	/18	/18	/28	/28

Read the following instructions carefully:

1. Complete the words by filling one letter in each box.

2. The timer indicates the maximum recommended time you have for the following passages.

X minutes

3. Work as quickly and carefully as you can.

4. When you have finished a page, go straight onto the next page until you finish the test.

5. Write your answers clearly and legibly. You will get no marks for illegible answers.

6. To change your answer, rub out your old answer completely and then mark your new answer clearly.

7. When you reach the end go back and check all your answers in the remaining time.

8. If you cannot answer a question, go on to the next question.

Good luck!

After you have finished this paper you can use the 11+ Peer Compare System™ to see how well you performed compared to others who have taken these tests. You can register by visiting www.ElevenPlusExams.co.uk/FirstPastThePost to post your results anonymously and obtain the feedback.

Fossils

Fossils are the preserved remains or **(1)** ☐mpre☐s☐ons of plants or animals and provide evidence that life existed on Earth millions of years ago. They are used by **(2)** p☐lae☐ntol☐gi☐t☐ and scientists to study the types of plants and **(3)** ☐nim☐l☐ which existed on Earth, and they can tell us a lot about **(4)** ev☐lut☐on. Although fossils can be found in many places such as on the beach and in **(5)** qua☐rie☐, in most cases, they are discovered by exhuming layers of **(6)** sed☐men☐ary rock formed of silt, sand, and mud that have **(7)** s☐lid☐fie☐ over time. It is when these rocks become eroded by forces of nature such as wind and water, that the fossils are **(8)** r☐v☐ale☐.

Baboons

The baboon is one of the most **(9)** pr☐val☐nt species of monkey found in Africa, and despite **(10)** d☐scern☐b☐e differences, is very closely related to humans. They are extremely societal creatures and dwell in large **(11)** m☐triar☐hal troops of 20 to a few hundred members. These predominantly consist of females who lead the members, their offspring and several **(12)** tra☐s☐ent males as they leave and change troops every few years. To its enemies, the baboon is considered to be dangerous and **(13)** ☐indic☐iv☐, but amongst a troop, its behaviour and relationships are worked out in a **(14)** r☐cipr☐cal, give and take, system. Unlike many other monkeys, baboons are **(15)** terr☐stri☐l and spend most of their time on the ground foraging for food or being **(16)** v☐gil☐n☐ of predators. For the most part, their diets are **(17)** he☐biv☐rou☐, albeit on occasion, they eat insects and prey on fish, hares and birds.

The Solar System

(1) S☐ie☐ti☐ts believe that the Solar System is 4.6 **(2)** b☐☐☐i☐n years old. Our **(3)** ☐ol☐r System comprises eight planets that **(4)** ☐r☐it the sun. It also has many **(5)** sm☐☐le☐ planets, comets, moons, **(6)** m☐t☐oro☐d☐, dust and gas. The largest planet is **(7)** ☐u☐it☐r, named after the Roman god, Jupiter, and is known to be the most **(8)** t☐rbu☐en☐ planet in the Solar System. This is because it **(9)** ☐pin☐ faster than any other planet creating an ever changing **(10)** wh☐rlp☐o☐ of storms. The third planet from the Sun, known as the Blue Planet, is **(11)** ☐☐rth and it lies 150 million kilometers from the sun.

Piranhas

Piranhas are **(12)** f☐esh☐ate☐ fish that inhabit South American **(13)** ☐iv☐rs. They are covered in scales that reflect sunlight and provide **(14)** c☐mo☐fl☐ge, thus preventing them from being spotted by **(15)** p☐edat☐☐s above the water surface. Their **(16)** p☐we☐fu☐ jaws and razor-sharp teeth have earned the piranha a **(17)** r☐pu☐ati☐n as blood thirsty, **(18)** f☐r☐ci☐u☐ predators that launch **(19)** f☐enz☐e☐ attacks on any large animal. The reality however, is that the **(20)** ☐i☐anh☐ is in fact a timid **(21)** sc☐v☐n☐e☐, that also has an appetite for insects, fish, fruits, seeds, birds, **(22)** aq☐at☐c plants and lizards. Generally, piranhas are of little threat to **(23)** ☐um☐n☐ and it is rare for them to attack people.

Vikings

The Vikings **(1)** h☐ile☐ from Scandinavia, a region which consisted of Denmark, Sweden, Norway, and Finland. They left their land in search of abundance and **(2)** a☐☐e☐t☐re. This period in **(3)** h☐st☐☐y was known as the Viking Age which began in the late 8th century and lasted for about 300 years. Vikings were **(4)** se☐far☐ng people who explored, invaded and **(5)** s☐tt☐e☐ in areas of Europe, Asia and the North Atlantic islands. Although they are widely known for their savage and **(6)** f☐ars☐m☐ raids of other lands, many of them were adept farmers and **(7)** pr☐l☐fi☐ craftsmen who were capable of building large ships from **(8)** p☐a☐k☐ of timber.

Morse Code

Morse Code is a method for **(9)** tr☐☐smit☐in☐ messages in which alphabetic letters are represented by a **(10)** c☐mbi☐atio☐ of long and short electrical **(11)** p☐lse☐, flashes of light, and sounds. Invented by Samuel Morse in the 1840s, it was initially used to send **(12)** ☐☐fo☐m☐ti☐n over a long-distance electrical **(13)** ☐om☐un☐cat☐☐n system called a telegraph. The most **(14)** r☐cog☐☐s☐d Morse Code phrase is the **(15)** di☐tr☐s☐ signal 'SOS', which literally means 'Save Our Souls'. Morse code is still used today by **(16)** ☐m☐t☐ur radio operators and the **(17)** Na☐☐ for communications between **(18)** n☐v☐l ships.

The Ancient Olympic Games

The first **(1)** ☐ly☐p☐☐ Games were part of a religious **(2)**

f☐☐t☐va☐ held more than 2,700 years ago in Olympia, **(3)**

Gr☐☐☐☐. They were known as the Greek Olympics and were **(4)**

ded☐c☐t☐d to the Greek God Zeus.

Before the **(5)** ☐☐me☐ began, any wars that were happening had to stop

for one **(6)** ☐o☐th so that the athletes could get to the **(7)** ☐it☐ of the

Games safely. Each city would pay for a few **(8)** at☐l☐tes to travel to the

event but there were many **(9)** r☐le☐ that had to be followed. All

competitors had to **(10)** p☐☐mis☐ that they had trained for at least

(11) ☐☐n months. As this **(12)** m☐an☐ that they would need to take

time off work to train, only **(13)** w☐al☐hy men could take part.

At first the Games only had one **(14)** ☐ven☐, which was a race from one

end of the **(15)** st☐d☐u☐ to the other and covered 170 metres, but over

(16) ☐im☐ other events were added. These included wrestling,

(17) ☐ox☐n☐, chariot racing and the long jump.

However, unlike the **(18)** m☐d☐r☐ Olympic Games, women were not

allowed to take part or even watch.

<u>Braille</u>

Braille is a reading and **(1)** ☐rit☐ng system used by the blind or visually
(2) imp☐ire☐ and was developed by Louis Braille in 1809.

At the age of three, Louis was involved in a **(3)** c☐t☐☐t☐ophi☐ accident
in his father's workshop when he accidentally **(4)** ☐ok☐d his eye with a sharp
tool and **(5)** ☐ubs☐q☐en☐ly lost his sight. When Louis grew older, he won
a **(6)** ☐ch☐l☐☐s☐☐p to the Royal Institution for Blind Youth in Paris. It
was here that he that he **(7)** e☐p☐r☐me☐te☐ with ways to create an
alphabet that could be read with the **(8)** f☐nge☐t☐ps.

In 1824, he **(9)** ☐nv☐nt☐d the Braille code that was based on a
(10) ☐ys☐em called 'Night Writing'. **(11)** So☐di☐r☐ used this to
communicate with one another during the night. Night Writing
(12) c☐mpr☐s☐d of lots of dots and **(13)** d☐sh☐s, which Louis adapted so
that each character became a small **(14)** r☐ct☐ngu☐a☐ block called a cell,
that in turn contained **(15)** m☐nis☐ul☐ raised dots.

The **(16)** ☐rr☐ng☐m☐☐t and number of dots enable Braille readers to
(17) di☐ti☐gu☐s☐ one character from another and each cell can be used
to **(18)** ☐epr☐s☐nt a letter of the alphabet, **(19)** ☐unc☐u☐t☐☐n
mark, number or an entire **(20)** ☐or☐.

Braille can be written in **(21)** ☐ume☐o☐s ways. Blind people can write using
(22) sp☐c☐a☐ apparatus called a slate and stylus; they can use a Braille

(23) ty☐ew☐ite☐, or even a computer with **(24)** ☐r☐ill☐ translation software and a Braille embosser - a **(25)** sp☐c☐f☐c type of printer that leaves a **(26)** tan☐ib☐e Braille cell imprint on paper.

Many years later, thanks to Louis' work and **(27)** ☐ed☐c☐ti☐n, millions of blind and **(28)** ☐isu☐l☐y impaired people around the world are able to read.

Mount Everest

With a **(1)** so☐ri☐g peak of 29,035 feet, Mount Everest is a place of

(2) u☐par☐ll☐led beauty and is the highest mountain in the world.

Situated along the border of Nepal, Tibet and China, its **(3)** tr☐nscen☐ent

height reaches five and a half miles in to the sky.

Everest forms part of the Himalayan mountain range that **(4)** trav☐rs☐s 1,500

miles across Asia.

The mountain is over 60 million years old and was formed by the

(5) c☐llisio☐ of the Indian tectonic plate pushing against the Eurasian plate

with **(6)** ☐ubst☐ntial force. This **(7)** ☐nst☐gat☐d a build up of pressure

between the plates, forcing the rock in between to push upwards. Even today,

the plates continue to shift and each year Mount Everest grows a quarter of an

inch higher. In 1865 it was named after Sir George Everest, the British surveyor

general of India and the first person to **(8)** d☐cum☐nt its height and locality.

With **(9)** f☐☐mid☐ble winds blowing up to 200 miles per hour and sub-zero

temperatures falling to below minus 40 degrees Celsius, Everest is an extremely

inhospitable mountain and presents climbers with an **(10)** a☐☐nd☐nce of

dangers. As well as freezing conditions which **(11)** habi☐ual☐y result in

frostbite and hyperthermia, avalanches are a constant **(12)** h☐z☐rd and the

shifting glaciers can **(13)** precip☐tous☐y create deep crevasses that climbers

have to be **(14)** v☐gi☐ant of.

However, one of the most challenging **(15)** p☐ril☐ the mountain poses is

the **(16)** sc☐rci☐y of oxygen and the altitude sickness. At the snow

capped peak of Everest, oxygen levels are only a third of what they are at

sea level and can have an **(17)** adv☐rs☐ effect on a person's breathing,

heart rate, muscle coordination, sleep, judgement and balance. In some

cases, **(18)** alt☐tud☐ sickness has proven to be fatal. Ascending the

majestic mountain is a **(19)** pr☐ca☐ious feat and one that has claimed

the lives of more than 200 people.

Between 1920 and 1952, there were **(20)** nume☐ou☐ attempts to reach

its summit but all were unsuccessful, and in one case led to the

(21) f☐te☐ul death of the famous mountaineer, George Leigh-Mallory.

The first people to conquer Everest and reach its **(22)** s☐mm☐t were Sir

Edmund Hilary and Tenzing Norgay, on May 19th 1953. They formed part of

the British **(23)** exp☐dit☐on led by Colonel John Hunt who had selected a

team of eleven exceptionally **(24)** pr☐ficien☐ climbers from all around the

British Empire. Upon reaching the summit, they could see at least a

hundred miles in every direction and witnessed **(25)** g☐or☐☐us views of

mountains, glaciers and high **(26)** plat☐aus. More than six decades later,

their historic **(27)** as☐ent remains to be one of the 20th century's most

(28) m☐ment☐us triumphs.

BLANK PAGE

FIRST PAST THE POST® SERIES

Cloze Tests
Book 1

Answers

As you complete each short test, remember that you can use the <u>11+ Peer Compare System</u>™ to see how well you performed in comparison to others who have taken this test.

You can register by visiting <u>www.ElevenPlusExams.co.uk/ FirstPastThePost</u> to post your results anonymously and obtain the feedback.

Your unique 16 digit access code is:

18ZK-W7X7-SEZU-1UFN

Word Bank Answers

TEST A

Page 2

The Altercation

(1)	emerged
(2)	abhorrent
(3)	altercation
(4)	escalated
(5)	talkative
(6)	solitude
(7)	longing
(8)	home
(9)	cacophony
(10)	recent
(11)	trepidation
(12)	adventure

Sharks

(13)	cartilage
(14)	enables
(15)	malicious
(16)	seldom
(17)	bulky
(18)	equipped
(19)	maintain
(20)	efficient
(21)	acute
(22)	refined
(23)	enormous
(24)	murky

TEST B

Page 4

The Moon

(1)	debris
(2)	collided
(3)	atmosphere
(4)	minute
(5)	waves
(6)	Gravity
(7)	Earth

Phobias

(8)	irrational
(9)	specific
(10)	phobia
(11)	acquired
(12)	heightened
(13)	arachnophobia
(14)	bizarre
(15)	anxiety
(16)	agitated

TEST C

Page 6

The Amazon River

(1)	longest
(2)	river
(3)	responsible
(4)	oceans
(5)	length
(6)	impressive
(7)	tributaries
(8)	species
(9)	savage
(10)	snake
(11)	shallow
(12)	gallons
(13)	second
(14)	equivalent

Gateway of India

(15)	monument
(16)	commemorate
(17)	emperor
(18)	visited
(19)	construction
(20)	commence
(21)	waterfront
(22)	ceremonial
(23)	heralded
(24)	independence
(25)	British
(26)	country

Word Bank Answers

	TEST D
	Page 8
	The Great Wall of China
(1)	scenery
(2)	heritage
(3)	world
(4)	resplendent
(5)	plateaus
(6)	perception
(7)	continuous
(8)	network
(9)	emperors
(10)	sections
(11)	enhanced
(12)	Dynasty
(13)	laborious
(14)	disgraced
(15)	conscripted
(16)	edifice
(17)	construction
(18)	cemetery
(19)	architecture
(20)	importance

	TEST E
	Page 10
	The Inuit
(1)	hostile
(2)	inhabited
(3)	winter
(4)	region
(5)	survive
(6)	solely
(7)	environment
(8)	paramount
(9)	nourishment
(10)	diet
(11)	meat
(12)	ice
(13)	relationship
(14)	prey
(15)	integral
(16)	sledges
(17)	frozen

	TEST F
	Page 11
	Florence Nightingale
(1)	statistician
(2)	destiny
(3)	fortunate
(4)	desires
(5)	vocation
(6)	nursing
(7)	wounded
(8)	located
(9)	unsanitary
(10)	mortality
(11)	hospitals
(12)	nature
(13)	earning
(14)	heroine
(15)	profound
(16)	campaign
(17)	regard
(18)	humanitarian
(19)	destitute
(20)	profession
(21)	training
(22)	arrangement
(23)	significant
(24)	procedures
(25)	recuperation
(26)	inventing
(27)	elected
(28)	era
(29)	influential

Multiple Choice Answers

TEST A	
Page 16	
Benjamin Franklin	
(1)	Founding
(2)	pivotal
(3)	versatile
(4)	celebrated
(5)	frequently
(6)	discoveries
(7)	electricity
(8)	prominent
(9)	designed
(10)	fire
(11)	worldwide
(12)	buildings
Volcanoes	
(13)	cavities
(14)	pressure
(15)	forcefully
(16)	vigorous
(17)	solidifies

TEST B	
Page 18	
Earthquakes	
(1)	peripheral
(2)	colossal
(3)	perpetually
(4)	conjoin
(5)	vigorous
(6)	emit
(7)	transpire
(8)	inaccessible
The Black Death	
(9)	pandemic
(10)	virulent
(11)	illness
(12)	squalid
(13)	associated
(14)	primitive
(15)	population
(16)	plague
(17)	alleviate
(18)	penitence

TEST C	
Page 20	
Alexander Graham Bell	
(1)	illustrious
(2)	celebrated
(3)	profound
(4)	device
(5)	current
(6)	astronomical
(7)	profitable
(8)	hydrofoils
(9)	legacy
Thomas Edison	
(10)	undeniably
(11)	pioneers
(12)	multitude
(13)	impact
(14)	motion
(15)	affordable
(16)	inquisitiveness
(17)	ardent
(18)	patented
(19)	prolific

Multiple Choice Answers

TEST D	
Page 22	
Ancient Rome	
(1)	flourishing
(2)	century
(3)	encompass
(4)	sovereignty
(5)	empire
(6)	conquered
(7)	advanced
(8)	unrestricted
(9)	copious
(10)	prosperity
(11)	life
(12)	paramount
(13)	controlled
(14)	typically
(15)	deities
(16)	temples

TEST E	
Page 24	
The Human Brain	
(1)	approximately
(2)	intricate
(3)	endeavour
(4)	organs
(5)	components
(6)	nervous
(7)	principal
(8)	mass
(9)	function
(10)	imagination
(11)	complex
(12)	navigate
(13)	hormone
(14)	prevent
(15)	generates
(16)	illuminate
(17)	recalling
(18)	connections
(19)	enhances

TEST F	
Page 27	
St Paul's Cathedral	
(1)	recognisable
(2)	dominated
(3)	resplendent
(4)	plagued
(5)	reconstructed
(6)	engulfed
(7)	invasion
(8)	cathedral
(9)	calamitous
(10)	edifice
(11)	accomplishment
(12)	purported
(13)	alleged
(14)	spire
(15)	Monarchs
(16)	worship
(17)	conducted
(18)	unyielding
(19)	dilapidation
(20)	besieged
(21)	lightning
(22)	distinguished
(23)	dome
(24)	architecture
(25)	catastrophe
(26)	ravaged

Multiple Choice Answers

TEST F (continued)	
(27)	charred
(28)	aftermath
(29)	commissioned
(30)	medieval
(31)	masterpiece
(32)	prodigious
(33)	prominent
(34)	ingenious
(35)	occupies
(36)	inscription
(37)	translates
(38)	notable
(39)	crypts
(40)	military

Partial Words Answers

TEST A	
Page 32	
Fossils	
(1)	impressions
(2)	palaeontologists
(3)	animals
(4)	evolution
(5)	quarries
(6)	sedimentary
(7)	solidified
(8)	revealed
Baboons	
(9)	prevalent
(10)	discernible
(11)	matriarchal
(12)	transient
(13)	vindictive
(14)	reciprocal
(15)	terrestrial
(16)	vigilant
(17)	herbivorous

TEST B	
Page 33	
The Solar System	
(1)	Scientists
(2)	billion
(3)	Solar
(4)	orbit
(5)	smaller
(6)	meteoroids
(7)	Jupiter
(8)	turbulent
(9)	spins
(10)	whirlpool
(11)	Earth
Piranhas	
(12)	freshwater
(13)	rivers
(14)	camouflage
(15)	predators
(16)	powerful
(17)	reputation
(18)	ferocious
(19)	frenzied
(20)	piranha
(21)	scavenger
(22)	aquatic
(23)	humans

TEST C	
Page 34	
Vikings	
(1)	hailed
(2)	adventure
(3)	history
(4)	seafaring
(5)	settled
(6)	fearsome
(7)	prolific
(8)	planks
Morse Code	
(9)	transmitting
(10)	combination
(11)	pulses
(12)	information
(13)	communication
(14)	recognised
(15)	distress
(16)	amateur
(17)	Navy
(18)	naval

Partial Words Answers

	TEST D	
	Page 35	
	The Ancient Olympic Games	
(1)	Olympic
(2)	festival
(3)	Greece
(4)	dedicated
(5)	Games
(6)	month
(7)	city
(8)	athletes
(9)	rules
(10)	promise
(11)	ten
(12)	meant
(13)	wealthy
(14)	event
(15)	stadium
(16)	time
(17)	boxing
(18)	modern

	TEST E
	Page 36
	Braille
(1)	writing
(2)	impaired
(3)	catastrophic
(4)	poked
(5)	subsequently
(6)	scholarship
(7)	experimented
(8)	fingertips
(9)	invented
(10)	system
(11)	Soldiers
(12)	comprised
(13)	dashes
(14)	rectangular
(15)	miniscule
(16)	arrangement
(17)	distinguish
(18)	represent
(19)	punctuation
(20)	word
(21)	numerous
(22)	special
(23)	typewriter
(24)	Braille
(25)	specific
(26)	tangible
(27)	dedication
(28)	visually

	TEST F
	Page 38
	Mount Everest
(1)	soaring
(2)	unparalleled
(3)	transcendent
(4)	traverses
(5)	collision
(6)	substantial
(7)	instigated
(8)	document
(9)	formidable
(10)	abundance
(11)	habitually
(12)	hazard
(13)	precipitously
(14)	vigilant
(15)	perils
(16)	scarcity
(17)	adverse
(18)	altitude
(19)	precarious
(20)	numerous
(21)	fateful
(22)	summit
(23)	expedition
(24)	proficient
(25)	glorious
(26)	plateaus
(27)	ascent
(28)	momentous